This book is all about a
awesome Chair Yogi calle

Once upon a time, you...

a **CHAIR YOGA** adventure
where you choose what happens!

MARIA OLIVER

ISBN: 978-1-8383024-2-9

DEDICATION

Thank you…

to my yoga class members who continue to teach me every day;

to Lucas and Seren for your brilliant suggestions;

to Andrew for your quiet confidence and unquestioning support;

to Lizzie Martell Illustration for your encouragement,
help, and technical and visual wizardry;

to the children and their parents and carers who tried this book out first;

to everyone who bought a copy of my first book
and made me believe I could do it again.

FOREWORD

I wrote the original *Once Upon a Time, You…* book because I love using story books in my children's yoga classes!

Writing a Chair Yoga edition felt important to me because sometimes it isn't possible for people to get down onto a mat to practice yoga. Chair Yoga can be just as strenuous, relaxing, fun and beneficial as yoga on a mat.

The children in the illustrations are shown sitting on colourful blocks. You can sit on whatever you like for chair yoga: classroom chairs, wheelchairs, cushions… sitting with the knees a little lower than the hips means that you sit in a more active way, rather than slouched backwards.

Yoga is for Every Body and also for every situation. I wanted to give all children an opportunity to be inside a yoga adventure story, add their own ideas, and have control over what happens.

I hope that this book gives all children a loosely structured story, within which they can use their imaginations, move their bodies, and make it a story that is unique to them.

HOW TO ENJOY THIS BOOK

This book is all about your child and they choose what happens – even when it's time for the story to end!

Do as many poses on each page as your child feels like doing.

Alignment in children's yoga does not have to be perfect. It doesn't matter if their version of a pose doesn't look quite like the picture. Their best effort is good enough.

Your child should always feel comfortable. For some poses I've suggested more than one version, so your child can choose what feels right for them.

The pictures sometimes suggest using props. This might be another chair, or a table or wall in front of the child. Use whatever you have to hand to make your child comfortable.

When doing an asymmetrical pose, suggest to your child that they repeat it on the other side.

Your child might come up with their own yoga poses or ideas of what can happen next.

Your child can make the story as long or as short as they like. They can repeat pages or swap endings. It could go on forever…!

Watch your child to see if they're still interested or if they're getting tired.

WARNING:

This book is designed to inspire your child to **MOVE**!

Tucking them up in bed first may be **FUTILE**!

Once upon a time,
you were climbing up a mountain.
As you reached the top
you found that you got
slower and more tired,
slower and more tired…

March your feet up and down
as you climb uphill.

When you reached
the top of the mountain,
you sat in seated Mountain pose
with two heavy feet on the ground,
arms loose by your sides,
feeling steady and still.

You saw something flying towards you.
Leaning forward,
you stretched your arms out wide,
to see if you could gently flap them
like wings.

What
was
flying
towards
you?

Was it a
Golden Eagle?
Go to page 10.

Was it a Dragon?
Go to page 12.

Was it a
Flying Horse?
Go to page 14.

A Golden Eagle was flying towards you!

Can you twist yourself into Eagle pose?

The Eagle was carrying a beautiful golden egg. Curl up tight in Child's pose, like the egg.

The Eagle landed and showed you the egg.
"I need your help!" the Eagle said.
"I must find somewhere safe for my egg to hatch.
Will you be my friend and fly with me?"

"Of course," you replied, and
stretched your arms out to fly away
with your new friend.

Where did you fly?

To a Forest? Go to page 16.
Or a Pirate Ship? Go to page 20.
Or a Royal Palace? Go to page 22.

A Dragon was flying towards you!

Imagine breathing out fire in Dragon pose.

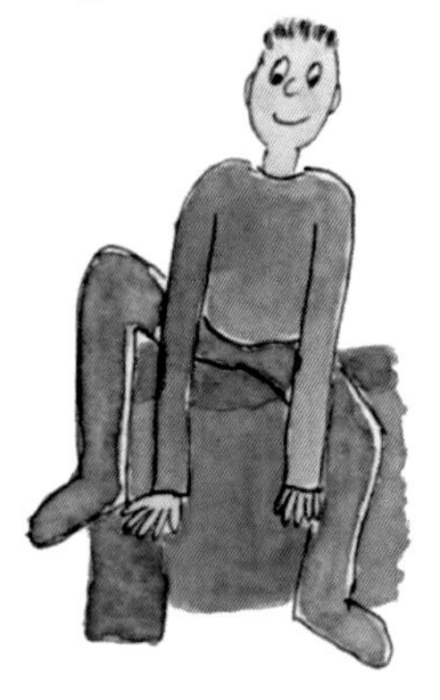

The Dragon landed and shouted:
"An enemy! Fight me if you are brave enough!"
It reared up and breathed out fire.

Feeling brave,
you stepped
one foot forward
into Warrior 1,
shouting
"You don't scare me!"

The Dragon was surprised.
"You are braver than I thought,"
it said. "Maybe you can help me
find some treasure.
Will you be my friend and fly with me?"

"Of course," you replied.
The Dragon lowered its head
so that you could
climb onto its back.
It spread out its wings
and together you took off.

Where did you fly?

To a Royal Palace? Go to page 22.
Or a Pirate Ship? Go to page 20.
Or Antarctica? Go to page 24.

A Horse with wings was flying towards you!

Reach out long, graceful wings and press into your feet in Horse pose.

Can you make your wings smaller so that you are a flying foal?

The Horse landed next to you.
"My Foal has run away!" it said.
"The naughty thing
has just learnt to fly,
and escapes
whenever I get close.
I need someone
with strong arms
to help me.
Will you be my friend
and fly with me?"

"Of course," you replied.
The Horse stood still
while you climbed on its back,
stretched out its wings and took off.

Where did you fly?
To a Beach? Go to page 18.
Or a Forest? Go to page 16.
Or Antarctica? Go to page 24.

You and your friend landed
in a **FOREST**.
What did you find?

Tree

Butterfly

Pigeon

Your friend said:
"We need to keep looking."
Where did you fly next?
A Royal Palace? Page 22.
A Pirate Ship? Page 20.
Antarctica? Page 24.

Ready to finish?
Friends of Flying Horses
go to page 28.
Friends of Dragons
go to page 30.
Friends of Eagles
go to page 26.

You and your friend
Landed on a **BEACH**.
What did you find
here?

Dolphin

Turtle

Dog

Starfish

Crab

Your friend said,
"We need to
keep looking."
Where did you
fly next?
A Forest? Page 16.
A Royal Palace? Page 22.
Antarctica? Page 24.

Ready to finish?
Friends of Flying Horses
go to page 28.
Friends of Dragons
go to page 30.
Friends of Eagles
go to page 26.

You and your friend landed on a **PIRATE SHIP**. What did you see?

Mermaid

Treasure chest – open and shut!

Pirates in Warrior 2 pose!

Your friend said,
"We need to keep looking."
Where did you fly next?
A Beach? Page 18.
Antarctica? Page 24.
A Forest? Page 16.

Ready to finish?
Friends of Flying Horses
go to page 28.
Friends of Dragons go to page 30.
Friends of Eagles go to page 26.

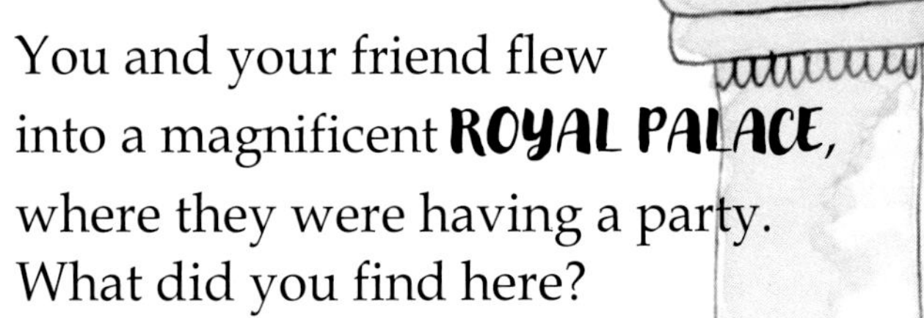

You and your friend flew into a magnificent **ROYAL PALACE**, where they were having a party. What did you find here?

Dancers

A cheeky puppy!

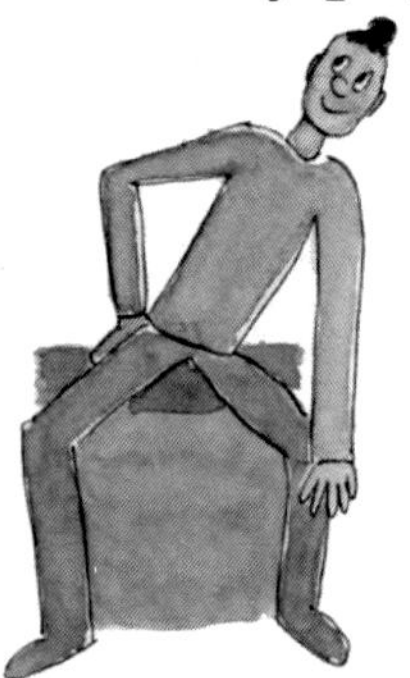

Pots of tea (triangle pose)

Your friend said,
"We need to keep looking."
Where did you fly next?
To a Forest? Page 16.
Or a Beach? Page 18.
Or a Pirate Ship? Page 20.

Ready to finish?
Friends of Flying Horses
go to page 28.
Friends of Dragons
go to page 30.
Friends of Eagles go to page 26.

You and your friend flew to **ANTARCTICA**! What did you find here?

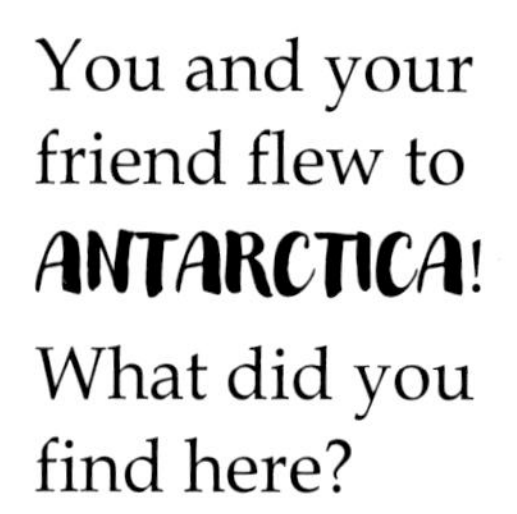

Penguins waddling

Penguins sledging

Seals

Whale

Snowflakes

Your friend said,
"We need to keep looking."

Where will
you fly next?
To a Beach? Page 18.
Or a Pirate Ship? Page 20.
Or a Royal Palace? Page 22.

Ready to finish?
Friends of Flying Horses
go to page 28.
Friends of Dragons
go to page 30.
Friends of Eagles
go to page 26.

Did you find a safe nest
for your friend's
golden egg to hatch?
"What about here?" you asked.
"It seems safe and nobody can see."
"Perfect!" cried the Eagle.
The Eagle set the egg down
and sat on it to warm it.
"It's hatching!" said the Eagle.

Curl up tight in Child's pose
like the Eagle's egg.
Now uncurl yourself
and stretch out your wings,
like a hatching baby eagle.

The Eagle stood and
you both watched the egg
as a tiny baby eagle
poked its beak out.

It gave a little croak.
"Hello, beautiful!"
said the Eagle to its baby.
It turned to you.
"I want you
to choose a name for it.
Thank you for all your help
on this adventure!"

Now imagine
yourself shrinking
small enough
to curl up in the Eagle's nest,
underneath its feathers.
You feel warm, cosy, and safe.
There may be noise going on
outside the nest,
but inside,
everything
is still.
Lie quietly
for a little while.

The End

Did you find the Flying Foal?
"Quick!" cried the Flying Horse.
"Use your strong arms,
before my baby flies away!"

You jumped forwards
to catch the Foal,
shouting "I've got you!"

Open your arms wide
then shut them tight
to catch the Foal.

"Thank you! Oh, thank you!"
cried the Flying Horse.

The Foal looked sorry.

"I've been so worried!" scolded the Flying Horse. "But I'm so pleased that you're safe!"

"I promise not to fly away again," said the Foal. "Well, maybe not today, anyway."

Imagine cuddling up to
the Flying Horse
and its Foal.
Their wings fold around you
so that you feel
safe and warm.
You can feel them
breathing slowly
so that you
breathe slowly too.

The End

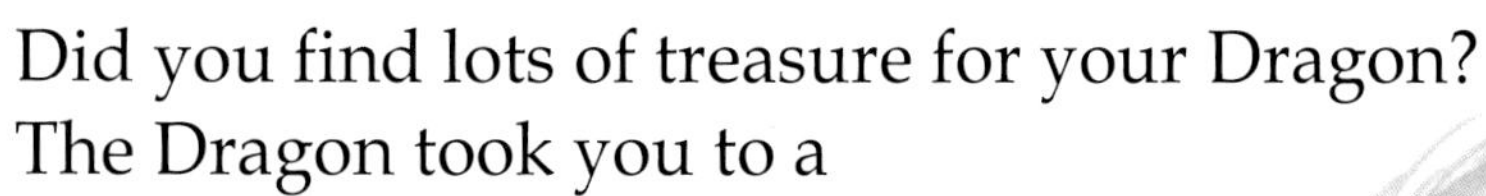

Did you find lots of treasure for your Dragon?
The Dragon took you to a
tiny island
in the middle
of a big ocean.

"We have collected lots of treasure,
and I thought it would
make me happy,"
said the Dragon sadly.
"But somehow, it doesn't."

It had been a long day.
The sun sank towards the sea,
and the sky turned a rosy pink.
Stretch your arms in the air
and bring the sun down.
As the sun sank lower, it shone on the sea.

"Look!" cried the Dragon. "Gold!"
"Isn't it beautiful?"

You watched the sun go down together,
until it got dark and the gold disappeared.
The Dragon looked sad.

"Don't worry," you said.
"It will happen again tomorrow."

"Really?" said the Dragon.
"What about the day after that?"

"The sun sets every night," you replied.

"Then I've found my treasure," declared the Dragon. "I can have gold every night before I go to sleep. Thank you for helping me to find it."

Imagine you are lying
on the beach of the tiny island,
curled up with your Dragon friend.
The sun is going down,
and the sky is pink and purple.
You can hear waves on the beach
and feel the warm sun on your face.
Everything is quiet
except for the sound of the sea.

The End

Yoga is amazing!

It can help us to feel good in our bodies and minds. Yoga is not just about doing yoga poses, though. Here are some other things you could try.

Breathing

Slow breathing is a super power!
When we slow our breathing down,
it helps us to feel calm.
We can focus best on our breathing
when we sit up tall.
Start off by shuffling from one sitting bone
to the other, then sit with both sitting bones
on your seat. Imagine that your head is
a balloon floating upwards.
Now breathe slowly into your belly.

Ocean breathing makes a lovely
relaxing sound, like waves on a beach.
Breathe in through your nose,
and when you breathe out softly say
'Shhhh....'
Keep saying 'Shhh...' until you run out of breath.
Then slowly breathe in through your nose again.

You can make the sound of a stormy sea, with
loud crashing waves, and then go back
to making the sound of gentle waves on a beach.

Tummy Surfing helps you to breathe
into your tummy so that you feel relaxed.
Lean back and let your tummy
rise and fall as you breathe in and out.
Imagine that your tummy is a wave
going up and down.
Maybe you can imagine yourself
floating up and down on waves
as you breathe in and out, or put a toy
on your tummy and let them go surfing.

Bee breath is a noisy humming breath!
Breathe in through your nose,
and when you breathe out,
hum until you run out of breath.
Then breathe in through your nose again
and hum as you breathe out.
This sounds amazing in a room
with other people doing the same thing.

Imagine you are blowing a **Dandelion head**!
Breathe in through your nose,
and breathe out gently through your mouth,
as if you are blowing on a dandelion head.
You want to blow so gently
that only a few of the seeds float away at a time.

Positive Affirmations

When we say kind things to ourselves,
it makes us feel better inside.
We often say mean things to ourselves,
which aren't really fair.
Have you ever said "I'm so stupid",
or "I'm always getting things wrong",
or "I can't do anything right"?
Let's try saying kind things to ourselves instead.
On the next two pages, you can cut out
some positive affirmations and look at them
every day.

Namaste

We say this word at the end of every yoga class.
We join our hands together at our hearts
and bow to each other while we say it.
It sounds like "Na Ma Stay".
Somebody once asked why we say this word
at the end, because we're not staying,
we're about to go home!
The word is in an old language from
India called Sanskrit.
It means that we are all connected to each other
because we are part of the same Universe.
We all have a bit of light inside us
and the light in me honours the light in you.

I am fearless

I am focused

From *Once Upon a Time, You...* (Chair Yoga Edition) by Maria Oliver
www.boxmooryoga.co.uk

From *Once Upon a Time, You...* (Chair Yoga Edition) by Maria Oliver
www.boxmooryoga.co.uk

I am loved

I am at peace

From *Once Upon a Time, You...* (Chair Yoga Edition) by Maria Oliver
www.boxmooryoga.co.uk

From *Once Upon a Time, You...* (Chair Yoga Edition) by Maria Oliver
www.boxmooryoga.co.uk

ABOUT THE AUTHOR AND ILLUSTRATOR

Maria is a Hertfordshire-based yoga teacher and member of the British Wheel of Yoga. She teaches yoga to children, adults, pregnant women and new mums. Maria has been writing stories and drawing pictures all her life, but the *Once Upon a Time, You…* original and chair yoga editions are the first published books that she has written and illustrated herself.

Maria trained in Positive Movement (including chair-based yoga) with Jo Marie, Yoga Teacher, and Judith Hammond, teacher of Dance, Alexander Technique and Moving Mindfully.
She has also attending training in Chair Yoga with Richard Kravetz.

Maria's first book, *Red Kites, Apples and Blood Cells* is a collection of relaxations for children and is available via **www.boxmooryoga.co.uk** and on Amazon. An Audiobook is available on iTunes, Amazon and Audible.
Maria is married with two children and two cats.

Search for Boxmoor Yoga on social media and YouTube!